Healing Mandalas

igloobooks

igloobooks

Published in 2016
by Igloo Books Ltd
Cottage Farm
Sywell
NN6 0BJ
www.igloobooks.com

Designed by Charlie Wood-Penn
Edited by Natalie Baker

Cover images: © iStock
Interiors illustrated by BOOKWORKS.IN

HUN001 0716
2 4 6 8 10 9 7 5 3 1
ISBN: 978-1-78557-900-4

Printed and manufactured in China

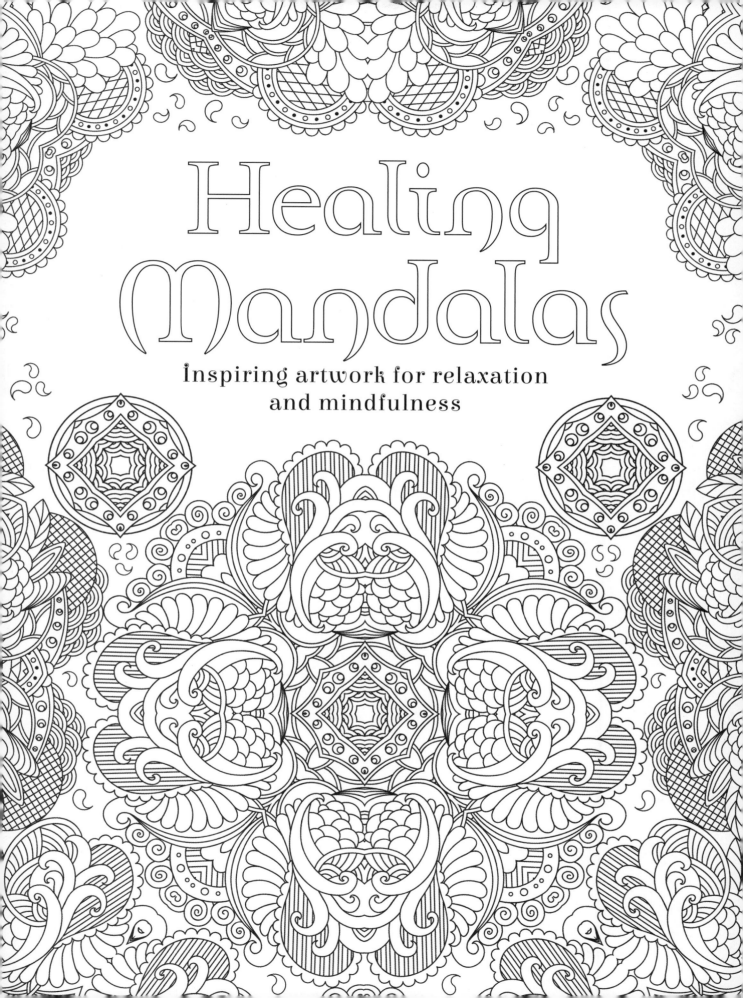

Healing Mandalas

Inspiring artwork for relaxation
and mindfulness

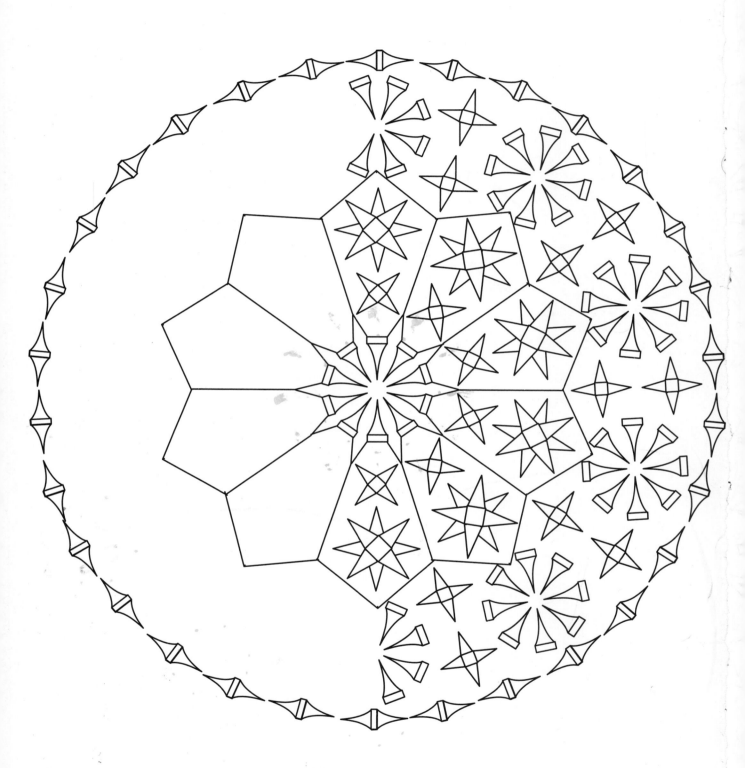

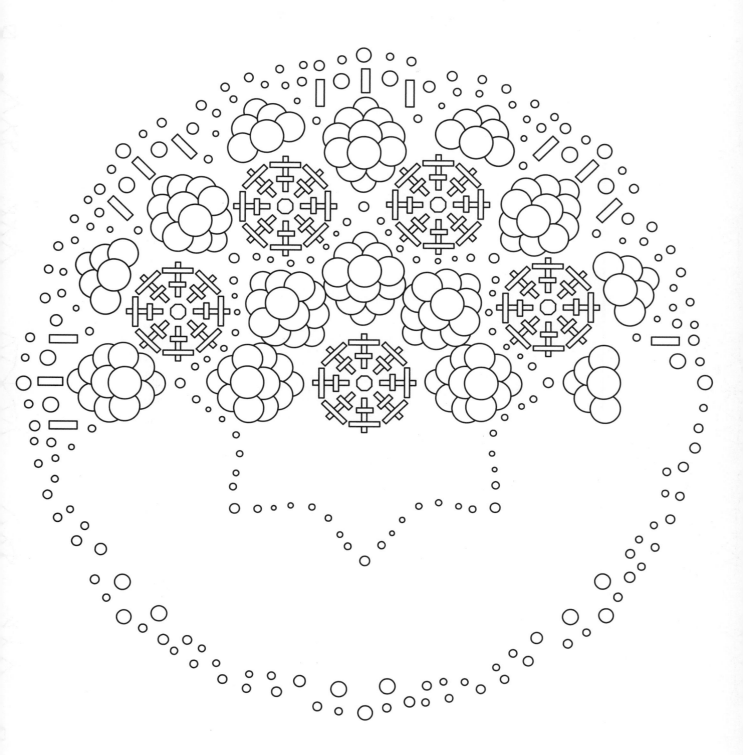

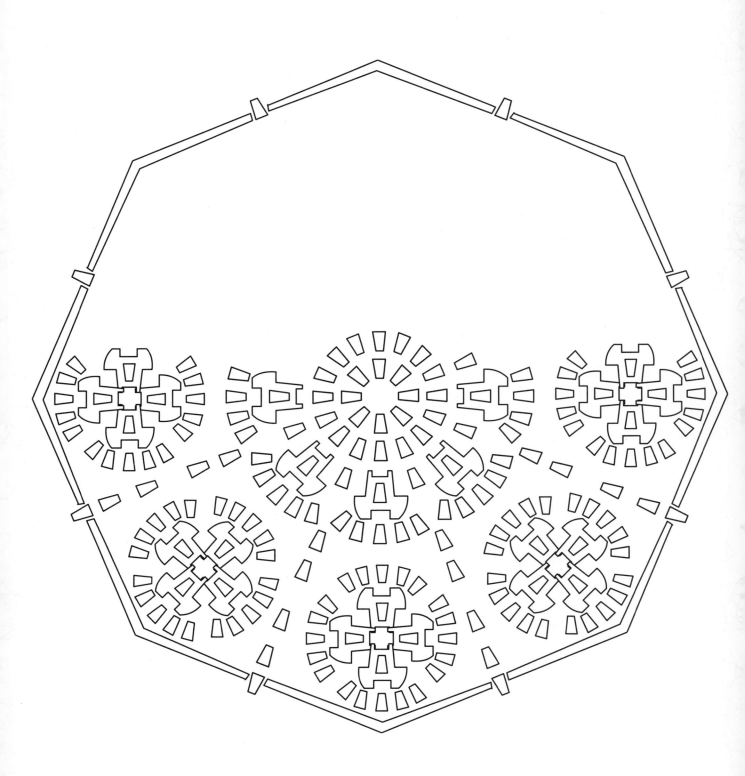

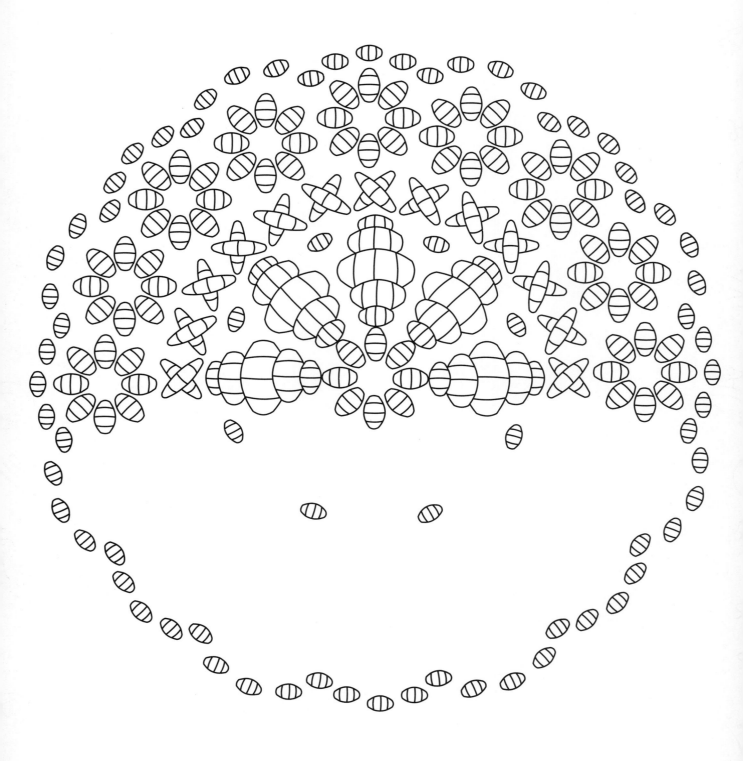

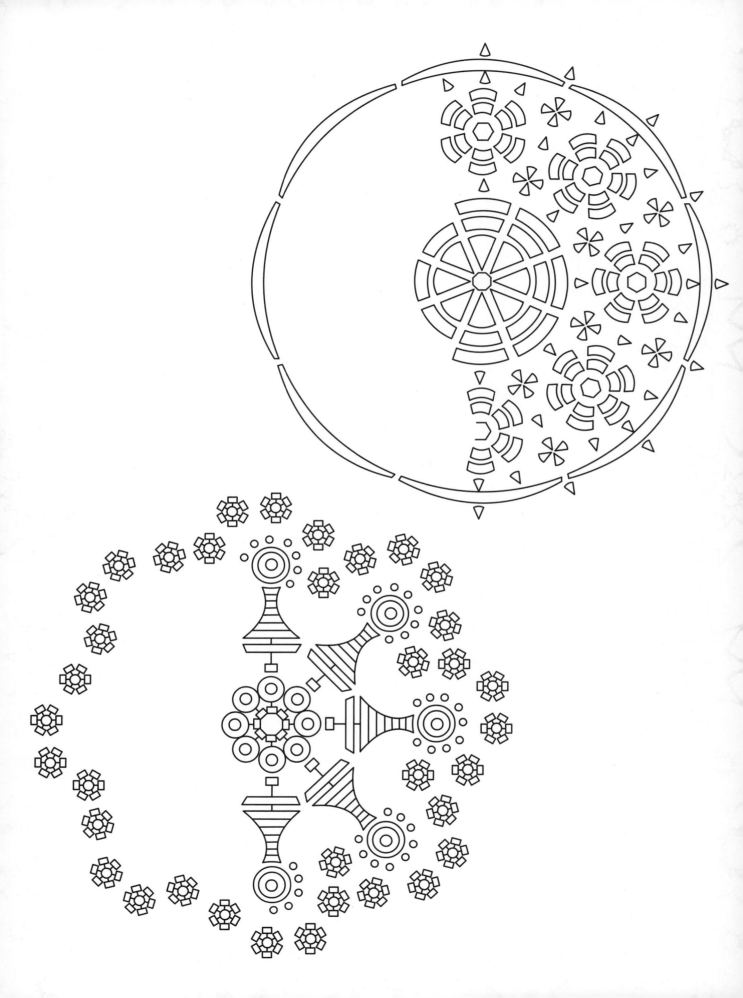

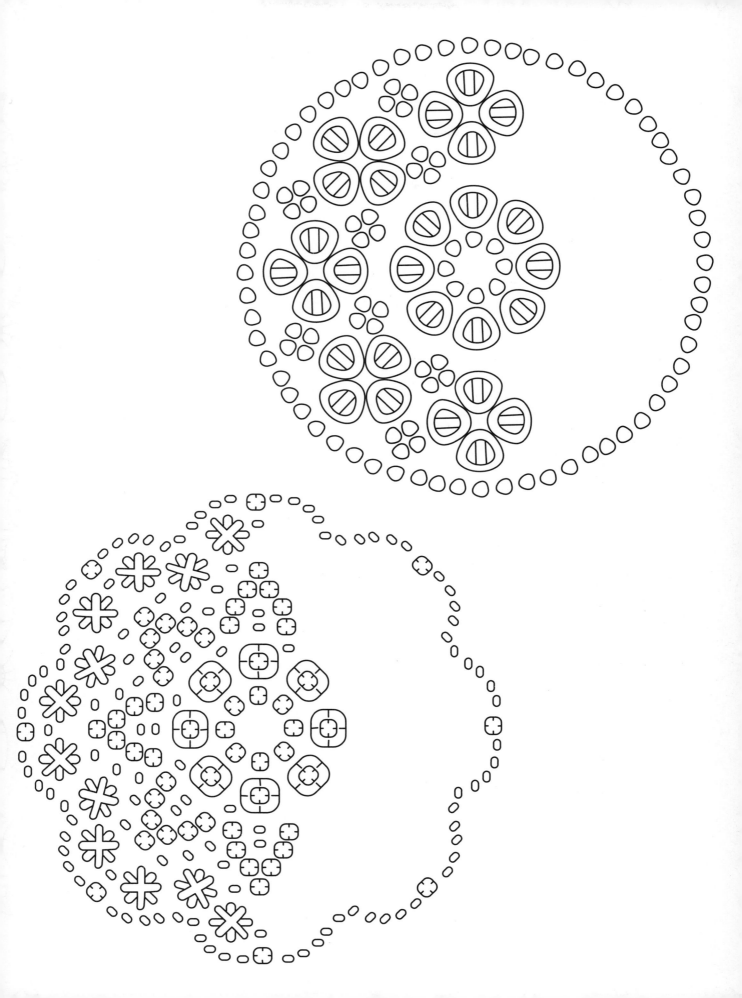

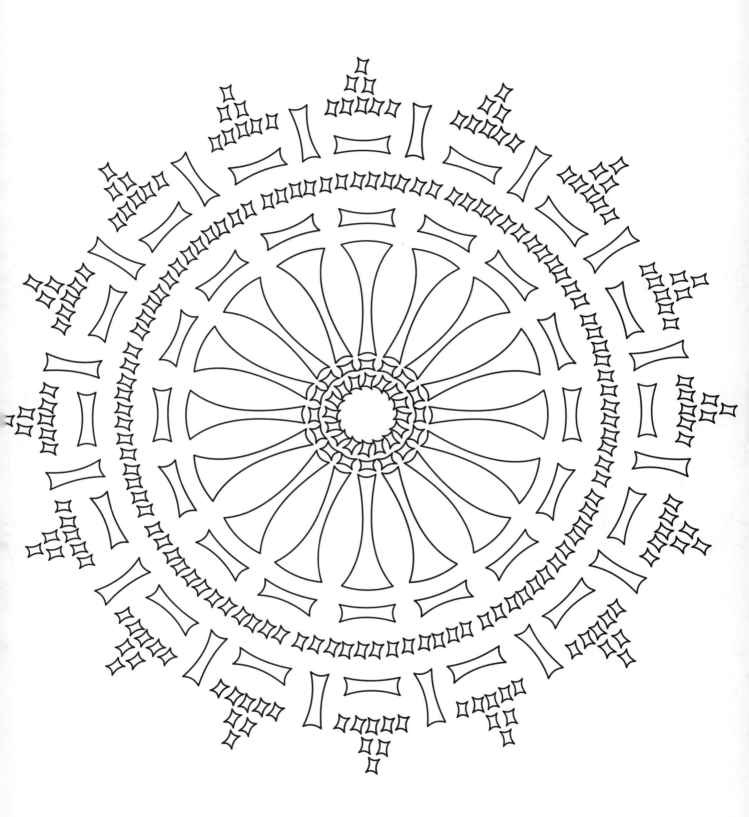

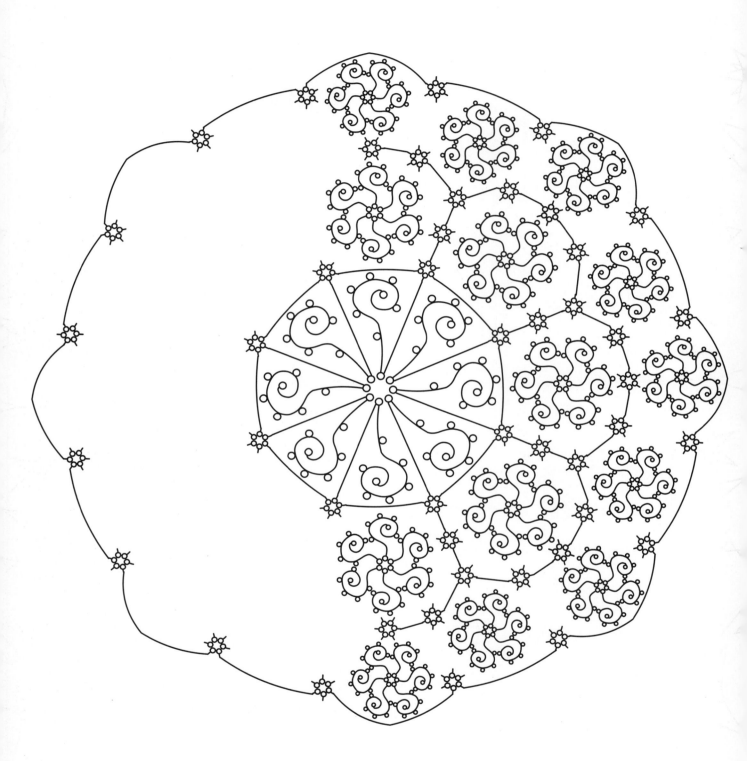

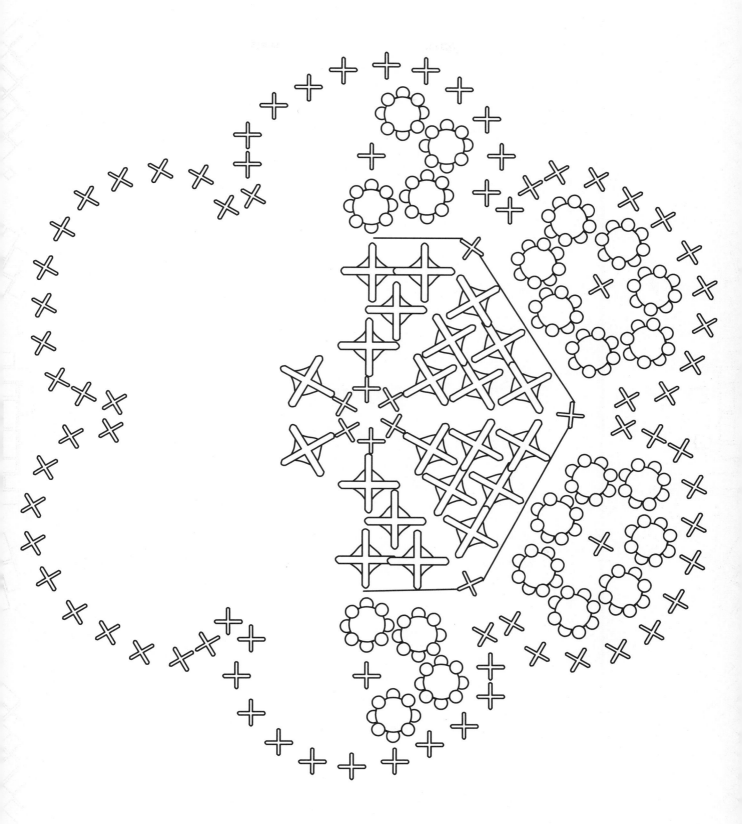

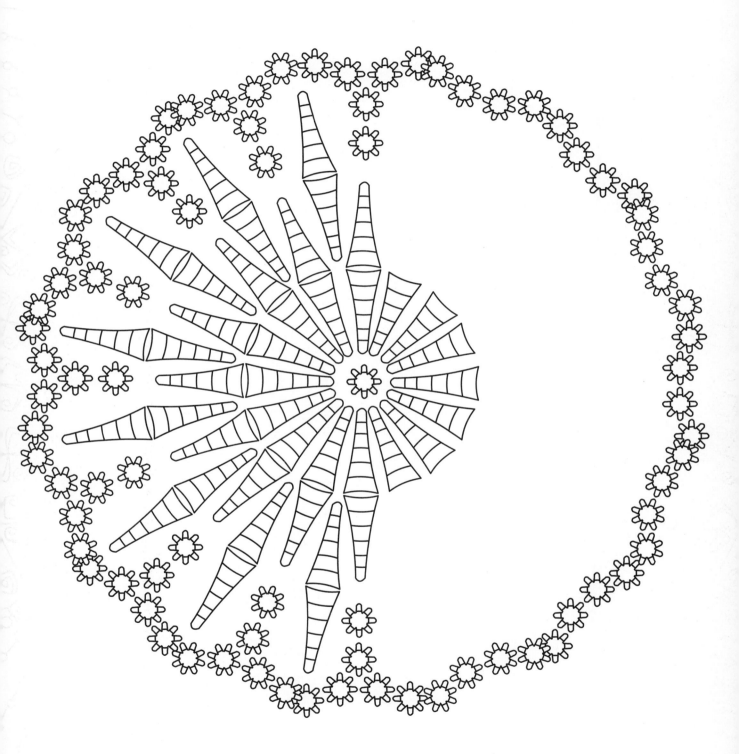

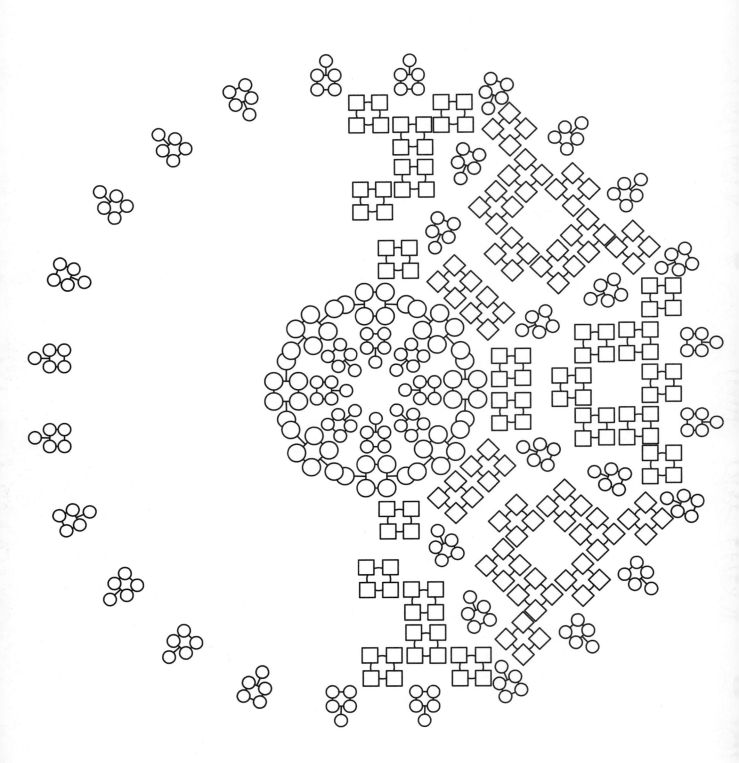

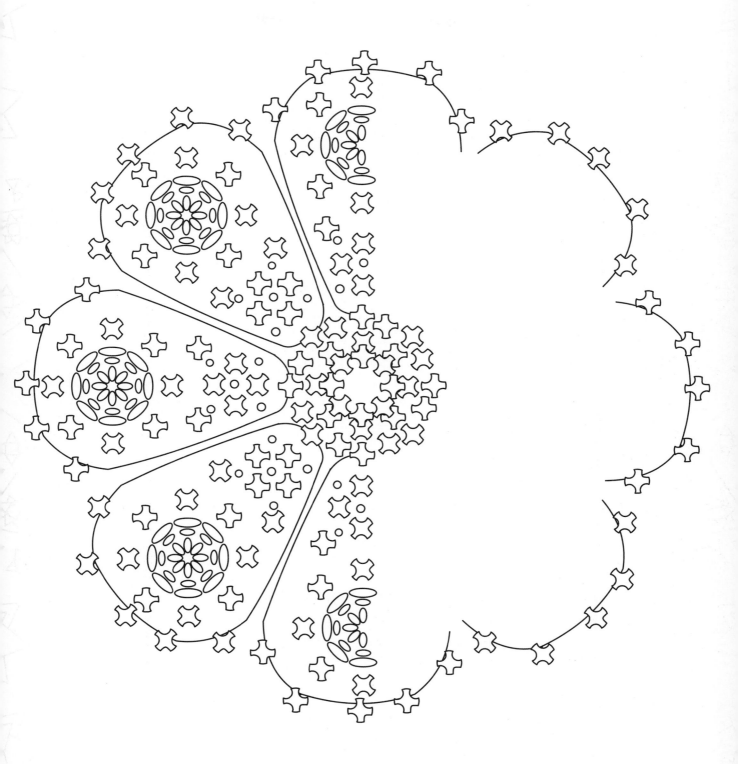

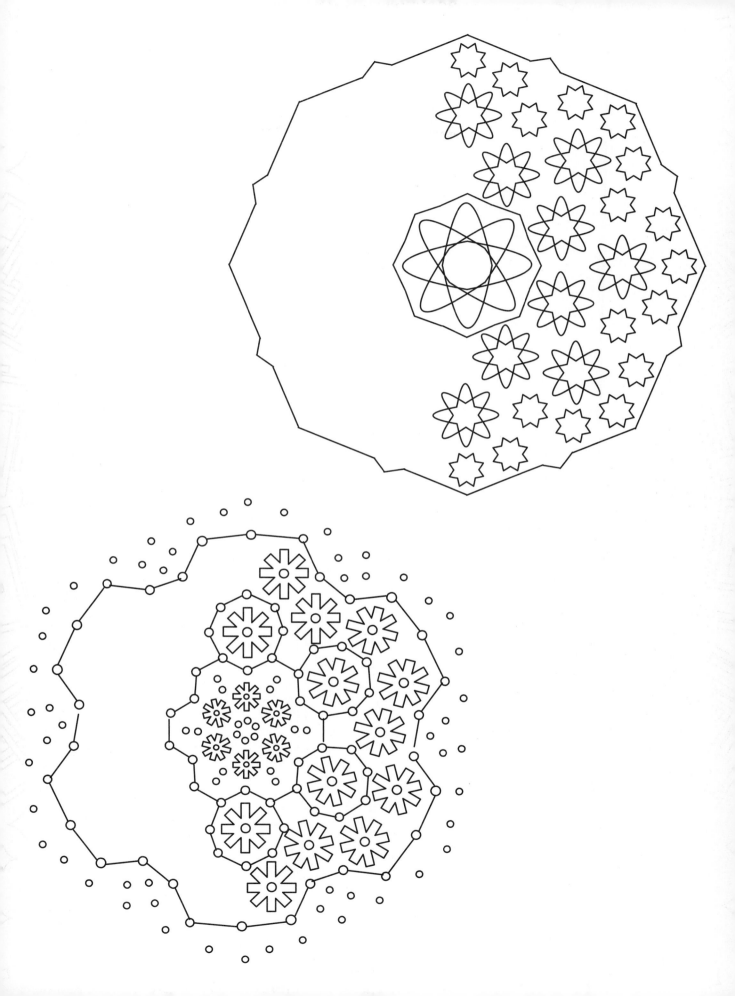

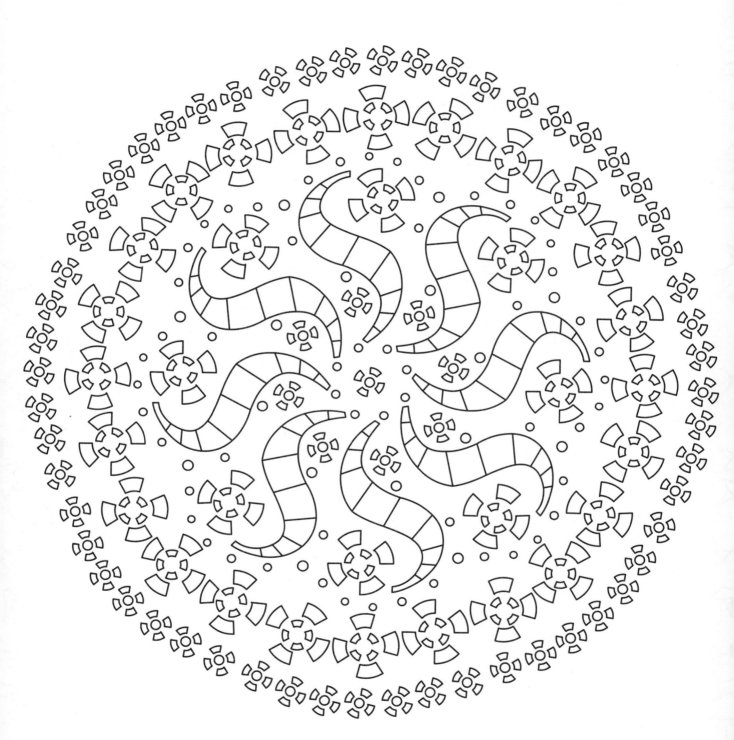

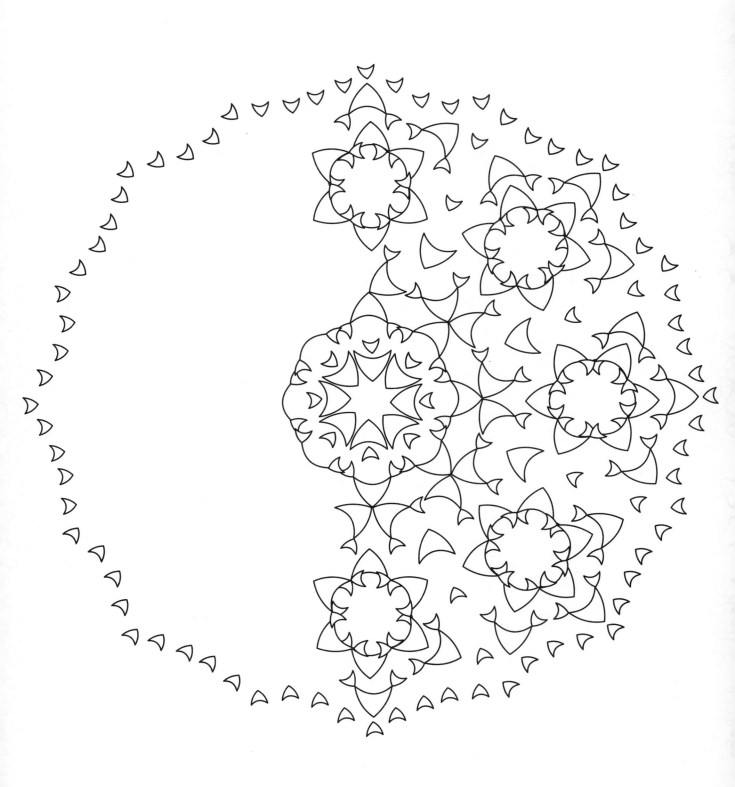

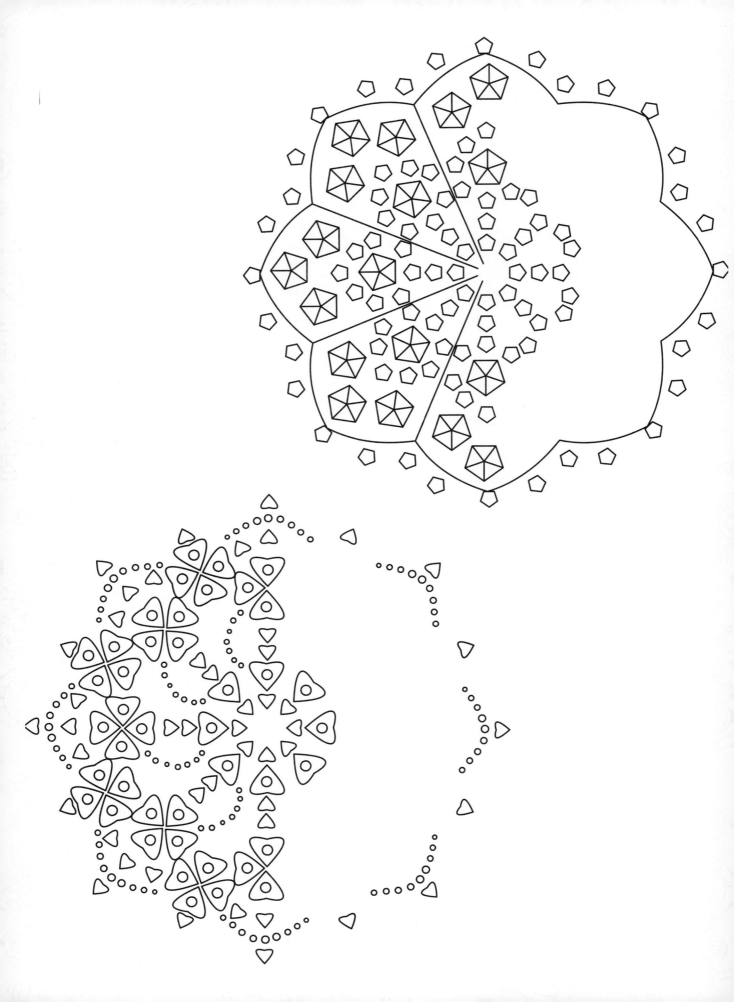

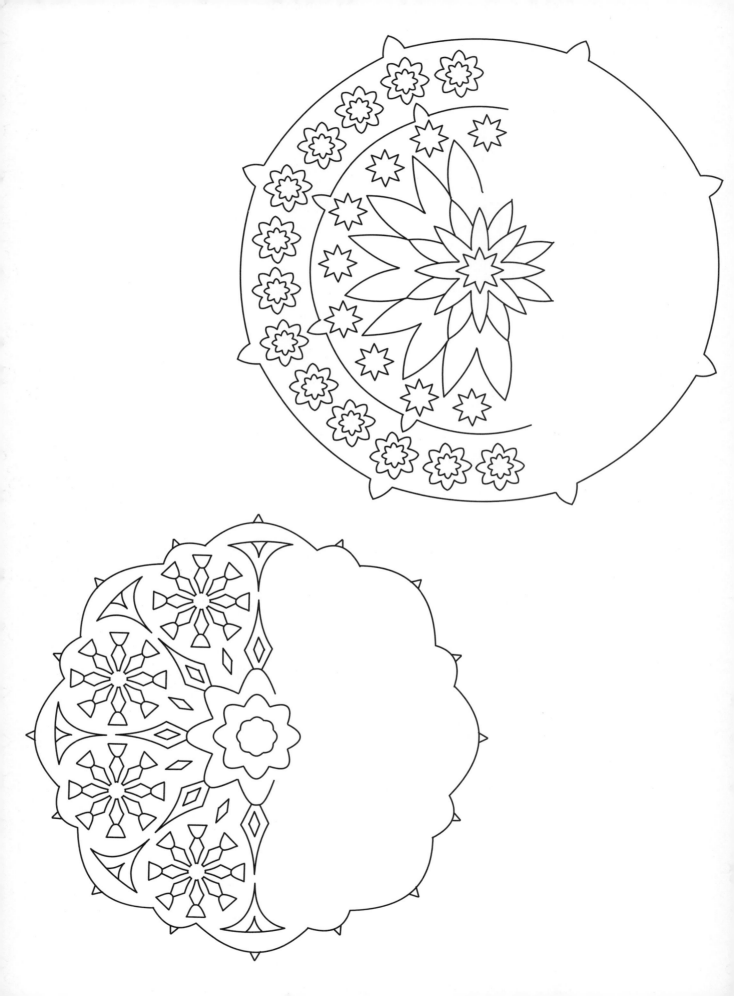